MW00650908

The Prince and the Pauper

Mark Twain

STUDENT PACKET

NOTE:

The trade book edition of the novel used to prepare this guide is found in the Novel Units catalog and on the Novel Units website. Using other editions may have varied page references.

Please note: We have assigned Interest Levels based on our knowledge of the themes and ideas of the books included in the Novel Units sets, however, please assess the appropriateness of this novel or trade book for the age level and maturity of your students prior to reading with them. You know your students best!

ISBN 978-1-58130-767-2

To order, contact your
local school supply store, or:

Toll-Free Fax: 877.716.7272
Phone: 888.650.4224
3901 Union Blvd., Suite 155
St. Louis, MO 63115

sales@novelunits.com

novelunits.com

Name _____

Clue Search

Directions: Collect information about the book for each of the items. Write the information down and then make some predictions for the book.

Information Source	Information Provided
Dedication	
Title	
Cover Illustration	
Teasers on the book cover or in the book jacket	
Friends' recommendations	
Reviewers' recommendations/awards won	

Your predictions for the book:

Name _____

Directions: Rate each of the following statements before you read the novel and discuss your ratings with a partner. After you have completed the novel, rate and discuss the statements again.

1 ——————— 2 ——————— 3 ——————— 4 ——————— 5 ——————— 6
strongly agree   strongly disagree

	Before	**After**
1. It is easier to adjust to sudden wealth than to sudden poverty.	_____	_____
2. Prestige and/or money make people more sensitive to others' needs	_____	_____
3. You can survive anything if you have one good friend.	_____	_____
4. We can control our own destiny.	_____	_____
5. Fate controls the destiny of each person.	_____	_____
6. Fantasies rarely develop into reality.	_____	_____
7. We pay too much attention to a person's outward appearance.	_____	_____
8. Children always imitate their parents' lifestyle.	_____	_____
9. Poor people have no ambition.	_____	_____
10. A child can never overcome a poor environment.	_____	_____
11. A child accepts his/her home life as the normal way to live.	_____	_____
12. Enough money will solve all of our problems.	_____	_____

Name _____

paupers (2)	offal (3)	rabble (4)	mendicancy (5)
melancholy (7)	obeisance (7)	mien (12)	raiment (12)
cudgel (13)	prodigious (16)	plebian (18)	patrician (20)
menial (21)	palter (29)	distemper (31)	stripling (32)
vagaries (37)	eccentricity (38)	panoply (39)	halberdiers (43)

Directions: Match each vocabulary word with the word or phrase closest in meaning.

_____ 1. paupers   a. immense

_____ 2. offal   b. odd behavior

_____ 3. rabble   c. sadness

_____ 4. mendicancy   d. a youth

_____ 5. melancholy   e. poor persons

_____ 6. obeisance   f. servant

_____ 7. mien   g. aristocratic

_____ 8. raiment   h. combined spears and battle axes

_____ 9. cudgel   i. trash

_____10. prodigious   j. begging

_____11. plebian   k. disordered state of mind

_____12. patrician   l. respect

_____13. menial   m. one of common birth

_____14. palter   n. mob

_____15. distemper   o. full suit of armor

_____16. stripling   p. appearance

_____17. vagaries   q. short, thick stick

_____18. eccentricity   r. bargain

_____19. panoply   s. clothing

_____20. halberdiers   t. whims

mummeries (48)	wenches (49)	commiseration (50)	canker (54)
usurper (55)	limpid (56)	rapier (59)	waif (62)
inane (64)	soliloquizing (66)	insolent (67)	alacrity (67)
suborned (70)	obsequies (83)	preamble (83)	ducal (84)
formidable (97)	veneration (103)		

Directions: In the chart below, (1) place a check mark in the column that best describes your familiarity with the word; (2) find the sentence in which the word appears in the text of the novel; (3) look up each word in the dictionary to find the definition as used in the novel.

Vocabulary Word	I Can Define	I Have Seen/Heard	New Word For Me
mummeries			
wenches			
commiseration			
canker			
usurper			
limpid			
rapier			
waif			
inane			
soliloquizing			
insolent			
alacrity			
suborned			
obsequies			
preamble			
ducal			
formidable			
veneration			

rue (108)	truculent (110)	blasphemy (113)	ironical (116)
epithets (119)	Providence (121)	uncanny (122)	pungent (123)
kine (126)	comely (127)	sagacity (130)	magnanimous (131)
judiciously (134)	patriarchs (136)	archangel (136)	impotent (141)
complaisance (142)	copse (142)	mortification (147)	infamous (149)

Directions: When you are trying to understand the meaning of a new word, it is helpful to have an example to which you can personally relate. For the word "rue" (p. 108), you might use the example, "the way I feel when I've said something to hurt someone's feelings." For the following words, list a synonym and a personal example to help you remember the word's meaning. The example can be from your own experience or from your imagination.

Word	Synonym	Example
1. truculent (110)		
2. blasphemy (113)		
3. ironical (116)		
4. epithets (119)		
5. Providence (121)		
6. uncanny (122)		
7. pungent (123)		
8. kine (126)		
9. comely (127)		
10. sagacity (130)		
11. magnanimous (131)		
12. judiciously (134)		
13. patriarchs (136)		
14. archangel (136)		
15. impotent (141)		
16. complaisance (142)		
17. copse (143)		
18. mortification (147)		
19. infamous (149)		

consternation (154)   decorum (154)   flogging (155)   undulation (161)
leal (165)   imperviously (169) miscreant (171)   taciturn (173)
seditious (176)   vagabond (183)   pillory (183)   sardonic (185)
fortitude (185)   evanescent (188)

Directions: Match each vocabulary word with the word or phrase that means the opposite.

_____ 1. consternation   a. disloyal

_____ 2. decorum   b. chair of honor

_____ 3. flogging   c. enduring

_____ 4. undulation   d. peacefulness

_____ 5. leal   e. respectful

_____ 6. imperviously   f. fear

_____ 7. miscreant   g. impropriety

_____ 8. taciturn   h. accessibly

_____ 9. seditious   i. giving public honor

_____10. vagabond   j. good person

_____11. pillory   k. nonresistant

_____12. sardonic   l. talkative

_____13. fortitude   m. homebound

_____14. evanescent   n. motionless

salaaming (191)   penury (192)   vassals (192)   rent (193)
largess (195)   effigy (196)   eulogistic (196)   transept (201)
apparition (203)   fealty (204)   dynasty (205)   musings (213)
torpid (218)   benignant (222)

Directions: Circle one word from each list that does NOT belong with the others. Briefly explain why that word does not belong.

1. salaaming	bowing	skiing	reverence
2. penury	wealth	poverty	want
3. vassals	landholders	vessels	serfs
4. rent	tear	rip	money
5. largess	philanthropy	bigger	gifts
6. effigy	likeness	resemblance	effort
7. eulogistic	statistic	praise	acclamation
8. transept	transfer	church	cross
9. apparition	phantom	supernatural	natural
10. fealty	faithfulness	fidelity	treachery
11. dynasty	hereditary	powerless	endowment
12. musings	frivolity	meditations	dreams
13. torpid	sluggish	dormant	powerful
14. benignant	favorable	detrimental	congenial

Directions: Answer the following questions on separate paper. The starred questions indicate thought or opinion or an activity. Use the answers in class discussions, for writing assignments, and to review for tests.

Chapters 1–3, pp. 1-15

1. Identify Tom Canty and Edward Tudor and explain the circumstances of their births and where they now live.

2. *Describe the members of Tom's family and explain how they interact with Tom. Who do you think is most important to him? Why?

3. Who is Father Andrew? Why is he important to Tom?

4. *How does Tom view his life? How would you view your life in similar circumstances?

5. What is Tom's recurrent desire and dream? What effect does this have on him?

6. How do Tom and Edward first meet? How does Tom get to go inside the palace?

7. *What are Tom's and Edward's "princely titles"? Explain why you think these are or are not appropriate.

8. What does Tom tell Edward about his life? What does Edward tell Tom?

9. Why do Edward and Tom exchange clothes? What happens after this?

10. *Prediction: What will happen to Tom? to Edward?

11. *Activity: Write bio-poems for Tom and Edward. Add to these as you learn more about the two boys. Pattern—Line 1: Name; Line 2: Lives (place)...; Line 3: Four descriptive words; Line 4: Relationships, i.e., Son of, Brother of, Friend of...; Line 5: Likes to...; Line 6: Feels...; Line 7: Needs...; Line 8: Gives...; Line 9: Fears...; Line 10: Would like to...; Line 11: Becomes...

Chapters 4–6, pp. 16-35

1. How is Edward treated at Christ's Church? What does he resolve to do as a result of this?

2. *What does John Canty do when he finds Edward? What do you think Edward will do when he gets to the Canty's home?

3. What happens when "Tom" tries to reveal his true identity to John Canty?

4. *How does King Henry VIII treat "Edward"? What do you think this reveals about the king?

5. Identify the Earl of Hertford and Lord St. John. Why are they important to Tom?

6. *How do Elizabeth and Jane Grey treat Tom? Which one do you think shows the most compassion? Why?

7. *Activity: Write a one- or two-sentence explanation of the metaphor, "The houses in Offal Court are swarming hives of poverty and misery" (p. 19).

8. *Activity: Sketch your impression of the metaphor, "The castle was a gilded cage" (p. 26).

Chapters 7–9, pp. 36-46

1. Why is Tom afraid to scratch his nose?

2. Why does King Henry want the Great Seal?

3. Who does the king send to Tom to get the Great Seal? How does Tom react to the search?

4. *Identify at least two changes in Tom's life during his first twenty-four hours as Edward. Which change do you think is the most important to him? Why?

5. *Prediction: Will Tom be able to convince the court nobles that he is not Edward? If so, how?

6. *Activity: Write a cinquain poem about royalty. Pattern—Line 1: the title, one word (noun); Line 2: two words to describe the title; Line 3: three words to express action concerning the title; Line 4: four words to express feeling(s) about the title; Line 5: one word that is a synonym for the title.

Chapters 10–11, pp. 47-61

1. How does the Canty family react to Edward's attempts to identify himself?

2. *What does Tom's mother do to test Edward's identity? What is the result? Why do you think she reacts as she does?

3. Who tries to defend Edward against his father and the mob? What is the result?

4. *How does Edward react to his vision of Tom playing the role of the prince? What do you think this reveals about Edward?

5. What happens that makes Tom the King of England?

6. Who defends Edward and rescues him from the mob at Guildhall?

7. *What is Tom's first official act after being declared king? What do you think this reveals about him?

8. *Activity: Draw a caricature that portrays the metaphor, "John Canty and his mother are swine" (p. 49).

Chapters 12–13, pp. 62-78

1. How does Edward react to the news of his father's death?

2. How does Miles Hendon react to Edward's declaration that he is the king?

3. What request does Miles make of Edward? How does Edward respond?

4. *How long has Miles been away from home? Why? How do you think he will be treated when he returns?

5. *Why does Edward disappear from Miles' room at the inn? What do you think this reveals about Edward?

6. *Prediction: Will Miles find Edward?

7. *Activity: Write a short paragraph or a poem based on Miles Hendon's self-appointed title, "I am a knight of the Kingdom of Dreams and Shadows" (p. 72).

8. *Activity: Draw a caricature of Hugh Hendon based on the metaphor, "Hugh is a reptile" (p. 69).

Chapters 14–16, pp. 79-106

1. Who helps Tom during his first day as king? How does Tom act in his new role?

2. *What does Tom suggest as a solution for the financial difficulties of the king's household? Explain whether or not you agree with his solution.

3. What is a whipping boy?

4. How does Humphrey Marlow feel about his role as whipping boy?

5. What request does Humphrey make of Tom? What is Tom's response?

6. *What are the crimes for which the man, woman, and young girl are about to be executed? How does Tom react to their plight? What does this reveal about him?

7. What does Tom discover about the man's crime? Why does Tom set him free?

8. How does Tom prove the innocence of the woman and the young girl?

9. How do the court officials react to Tom's dealings with the prisoners?

10. *Activity: Write a short poem beginning with the phrase, "If I were in charge of the world..."

Chapters 17–18, pp. 107-126

1. What happens to Edward after he leaves Miles' room at the inn?

2. What assumed name does John Canty take for himself, and what name does he give to Edward?

3. *Explain the type of people who make up the gang to which Canty takes Edward. How would you react to a gang like this?

4. *Who is the Ruffler? Why is he important to Edward?

5. Who is in charge of Edward in the gang? What does he want Edward to do?

6. How does Edward escape? Where does he spend the night?

7. *Prediction: Will Edward ever be able to return to his rightful place as king?

8. *Activity: Write a cinquain poem about the gang.

9. *Activity: Write a metaphor or simile poem that reflects Edward's happiness the night in the barn. Pattern—Line 1: noun (title); Lines 2–4: something about the subject (Each line should describe the subject in a different way.); Line 5: a metaphor that begins with the noun from line 1 or a simile that begins with the noun from line 1 and includes "like" or "as."

Chapters 19–22, pp. 127-151

1. *How do the peasants treat Edward? Give at least one example of the mother's failed attempts to find something he can do well. How would your mother react to a "visitor" like Edward?

2. What is unusual about the way Edward and the peasants react to each other as they share a meal?

3. Who is the hermit? Who does he think he is?

4. What does the hermit plan to do with Edward? Why?

5. *Why doesn't Miles rescue Edward when he comes to the hermit's cabin? Why do you think the hermit so easily tricks Miles?

6. Who frees Edward?

7. What is Edward doing when Miles finds him?

8. *Prediction: What will happen to Edward and Miles?

9. *Activity: Prepare an acrostic for the word "treachery." Pattern: Place the letters of the word vertically on your paper. Using each letter of the word as the first word of your response, write a word or phrase that tells something about treachery.

10. *Activity: Draw a caricature based on the metaphor comparing the hermit to a spider and Edward to an insect (p. 140).

Chapters 23–26, pp. 152-172

1. *What does Miles advise Edward to do when they go before the judge? Why do you think Edward follows his advice?

2. Why could Edward face hanging because of the stolen pig? How is his life saved?

3. *What does Miles threaten to tell the judge about the constable? What is the result of this confrontation? What do you think this reveals about Miles?

4. What does Miles anticipate will happen when he returns to Hendon Hall?

5. What actually happens at Hendon Hall?

6. *What does Miles learn about his father? his older brother? Edith? How do you think this makes him feel?

7. What does Edith reveal to Miles about Hugh?

8. *Prediction: What will happen to Miles and Edward after they are taken to prison?

9. *Activity: Write a note from Edward to his uncle, the Earl of Hertford, in which he explains his true identity.

Chapters 27–29, pp. 173-189

1. How long are Miles and Edward in prison? Describe the prison.

2. Who is Blake Andrews? What does he reveal to Miles about the Hendon family?

3. What does Andrews tell Miles about the English court?

4. *What "crime" have the two women committed? What is their punishment? Explain how their plight makes you feel.

5. How does Edward react to their punishment?

6. What punishment does Miles receive? How does Edward react?

7. How does Edward feel toward Miles for taking the punishment for him? What does Edward do?

8. What does Miles decide to do after being released from prison? Who does he think might help him?

9. *Prediction: What will happen to Edward in London? to Miles?

10. *Activity: Write a rhyme, set to the tune of "London Bridge" about Miles' and Edward's experiences on the London Bridge.

Chapters 30–32, pp. 190-212

1. Describe Edward and Tom during the time after they switch identities and before the coronation.

2. How has Tom adjusted to his role as king?

3. Does Tom ever think about Edward or his mother and sisters? If so, how do the memories make him feel?

4. *How does Tom react when his mother recognizes him at the coronation? What do you think this reveals about him?

5. When Tom declares the identity of his mother, how does the duke react?

6. When does Edward appear at the coronation? What happens?

7. How does the Lord Protector plan to prove whether or not Edward is the king? What is the result of this test?

8. How does Edward act when he is finally crowned king? How does he treat Tom?

9. *Activity: Design a Great Seal that shows your characteristics.

Chapter 33–Conclusion, pp. 212-222

1. How are Miles and Edward reunited? What is the key piece of evidence that links Miles and Edward together?

2. Explain what happens to the following characters in the denouement: King Edward VI, Tom, Miles, Tom's mother and sisters, Hugh Hendon, Edith, John Canty.

3. *Activity: Sketch Tom's "quaint but rich" clothing (p. 218).

4. *Activity: Draw a caricature of Miles based on the metaphor comparing him to a "stately scarecrow" (p. 216).

Attribute Web

Directions: Trace the following web and use in two ways: to show what Edward is like as the prince and what he is like as the pauper. Fill in the blanks with words and phrases which tell how he acts and looks, as well as what he says and feels.

Acts	Feels
_____	_____
_____	_____
_____	_____
_____	_____
_____	_____
_____	_____
_____	_____

Edward

Looks	Says
_____	_____
_____	_____
_____	_____
_____	_____
_____	_____
_____	_____
_____	_____

Name _____

Attribute Web

Directions: Trace the following web and use in two ways: to show what Tom Canty is like as the pauper and what he is like as the prince. Fill in the blanks with words and phrases which tell how he acts and looks, where he lives, what he says and feels, and others' actions toward him.

Acts	Feels	Says

Tom Canty

Lives	Looks	Others' Actions

Name _____

Characterization

Directions: Write words that describe Miles Hendon in the ovals around his name. Write details from the story that demonstrate each quality in the rectangles.

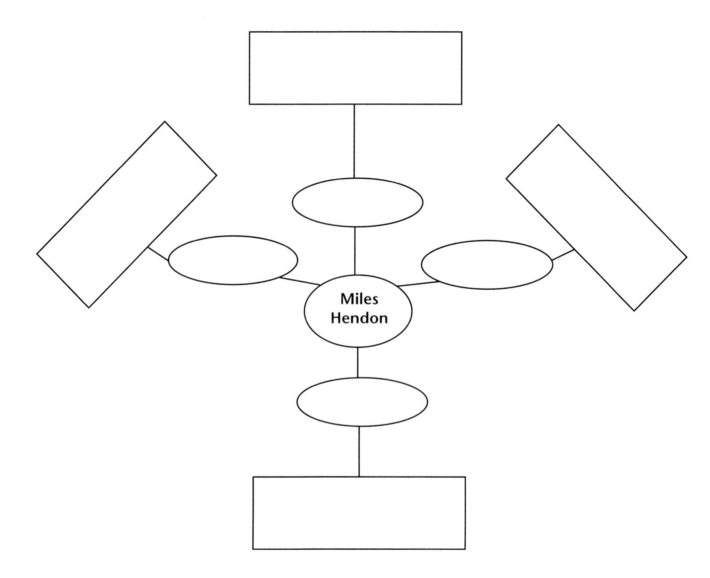

Name _____

Character Analysis Chart

Directions: List some of the characters who appear in the novel in the boxes below (other than Edward, Tom, or Miles Hendon). Working in a small group, discuss the attributes of these characters with other members of your group. In each character's box, write several words or phrases you feel describe him or her.

19

Sorting Characters

Directions: Similarities among characters are sometimes a clue to themes in the story. Place the book's characters in one or more of the groups below.

Victims	Victimizers	Fighters
Heroes	**Cruel Ones**	**Helpful Ones**

Name _____

Episodic Story Map

Directions: Fill in the characters, setting (time and place), problem, and solution. The flow chart boxes below are for the various episodes in the story.

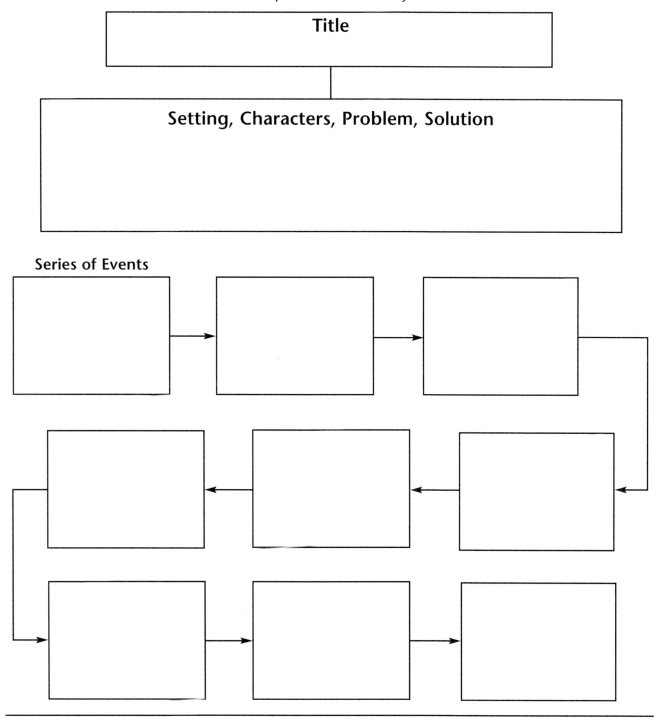

Title

Setting, Characters, Problem, Solution

Series of Events

21

Thematic Analysis

Directions: Choose a theme from the book to be the focus of your word web. Complete the web and then answer the question in each starred box.

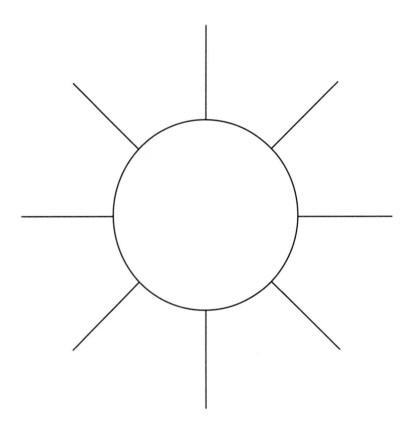

★ What is the author's main message?

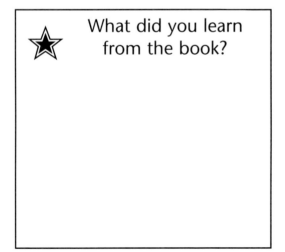

★ What did you learn from the book?

Name _____

Cause-Effect

Directions: Trace back to the causes of the unrest among the common people of England during King Henry VIII's reign. Fill in this cause-effect chart.

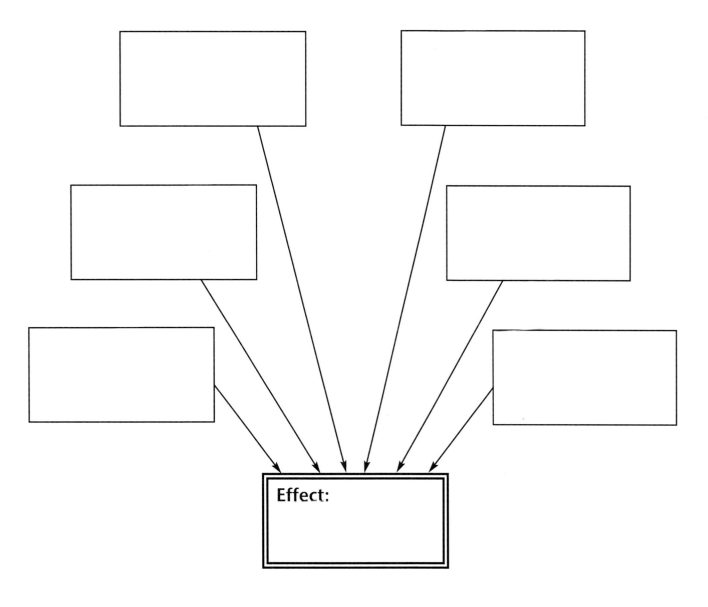

Effect:

Flow Chart

Directions: Fill in the boxes in the flow chart with the events portrayed in the story. In the ovals beneath, state what emotion and feeling is inferred.

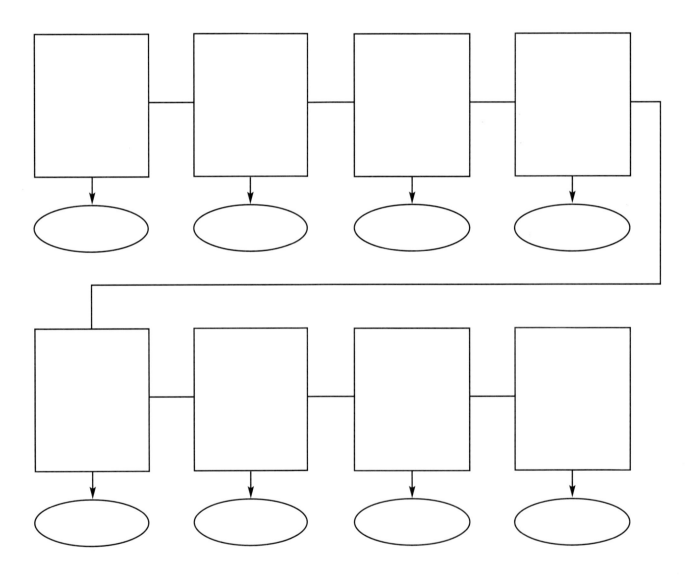

Name _____

Story Pyramid

Directions: Using the pyramid, write words or phrases to summarize the story.

Line 1: One word that gives the setting

Line 2: Two words that identify the two main characters (in order of their appearance)

Line 3: Three words that explain the problem

Line 4: Two words that describe character #1; two words that describe character #2

Line 5: Two characters that interact with character #1; three characters that interact with character #2

Line 6: Six words that explain the resolution of the conflict

Line 7: Seven words that summarize your impression of the book

1 _____

2 _____ _____

3 _____ _____ _____

4 _____ _____ _____ _____

5 _____ _____ _____ _____ _____

6 _____ _____ _____ _____ _____ _____

7 _____ _____ _____ _____ _____ _____ _____

Match each character with the correct identification.

____ 1. Tom Canty   a. good-hearted girls; unclean, uneducated, dressed in rags

____ 2. Edward Tudor   b. fat invalid; stern; loving father

____ 3. Bet and Nan   c. young boy whose father forces him to beg; educated

____ 4. John Canty   d. cares for a mistreated boy; teacher; kind

____ 5. Father Andrew   e. pampered royal prince

____ 6. Henry VIII   f. cruel thief

True/False

____ 7. Tom Canty is very unhappy with his life.

____ 8. Tom's mother beats him regularly.

____ 9. Tom dreams of seeing a real prince.

____10. Tom's meeting with Edward is accidental.

____11. Members of the royal court think Edward has lost his memory or gone mad.

____12. The Earl of Hertford and Lord St. John are Tom's "guardian angels" in court.

____13. Tom conducts himself without a flaw at his first royal dinner.

____14. Tom pleases the king by finding the Great Seal.

____15. Edward's father treats him kindly.

Name _____

Fill in the blanks.

1. _____ dies when he tries to save Edward from Mr. Canty.

2. Mrs. Canty tests Edward's true identity by_____ .

3. _____ comes to Edward's assistance and rescues him from the mob at Guildhall.

4. Edward grants his benefactor the privilege of_____ .

5. Tom's suggested solution to the kingdom's financial problems is to_____

_____ .

6. Edward is_____ when he hears of Henry VIII's death.

True/False

_____ 7. Tom's mother tells Edward she believes he really is the prince.

_____ 8. John Canty beats Edward when he fails to produce money from his begging.

_____ 9. Tom's first act as king is to save the Duke of Norfolk's life.

_____10. Miles Hendon is sure Edward is not the prince because he acts like a beggar.

_____11. Tom loves everything about being king.

_____12. Edward's whipping boy begs Tom not to send him away.

True/False

_____ 1. Edward's concern for Miles Hendon leads to Edward's recapture by John Canty.

_____ 2. Members of the gang to which Canty takes Edward are all lifelong thieves and robbers.

_____ 3. Hugo insists that Edward must join him in the "trade" of begging.

_____ 4. After escaping from Hugo, Edward takes refuge in the home of the town magistrate.

_____ 5. The peasants refuse to help Edward.

Write brief answers to the following questions.

6. What last name does John Canty assume to disguise himself from the law?

7. What is the gang's chief called?

8. What does the gang mockingly call Edward?

9. Who ties Edward up and intends to kill him?

10. Who frees Edward from his captor?

Complete the following statements.

1. Edward is accused of stealing _____ .

2. Edward is saved from hanging when the victim _____ .

3. Miles Hendon proves his ingenuity when he makes the constable _____

_____ .

4. Miles takes Edward with him when he returns to _____ .

5. Miles is warned that he must escape by_____ .

6. As his plan to set things right for him and Miles, Edward _____

_____ .

7. Miles learns the truth about the Hendon family from_____ .

8. Edward is heartbroken when he and the other prisoners must watch the execution of

_____ .

9. Edward's experiences with the other prisoners causes him to vow to someday_____

_____ .

10. Edward dubs Miles Hendon an earl because _____ .

True/False

_____ 1. Tom never learns to enjoy his role as king.

_____ 2. Edward watches the preparations for Tom's coronation.

_____ 3. Tom recognizes his mother in the crowd on Coronation Day.

_____ 4. Tom never acknowledges the truth about his mother.

_____ 5. Edward appears just after the Archbishop places the crown on Tom's head.

_____ 6. The Great Seal is an important key to the king's identification.

Match each character with his or her destiny in the denouement.

_____ 7. Tom Canty   a. loses his land and title; dies

_____ 8. Edward Tudor   b. receives title of King's Ward

_____ 9. Miles Hendon   c. is never heard from again

_____10. Hugh Hendon   d. repays favors to those who helped him

_____11. John Canty   e. receives title of Earl of Kent

A. Identification: Match each character or place with its correct identification. (1 pt. each)

____ 1. Tom Canty	a.	an abusive father and a thief
____ 2. Edward Tudor	b.	gloomy half-sister of the prince
____ 3. John Canty	c.	the king's palace
____ 4. Henry VIII	d.	Prince of Limitless Plenty
____ 5. Miles Hendon	e.	chief of a gang of ruffians
____ 6. Hugh Hendon	f.	wicked, evil heart; a beggar
____ 7. Offal Court	g.	uneducated, dirty, good-hearted sisters
____ 8. Earl of Hertford	h.	fun-loving cousin of the prince
____ 9. John Canty's wife	i.	forced into an unhappy marriage
____10. John Canty's mother	j.	"Prince of Poverty"
____11. Elizabeth	k.	manipulative, cruel brother
____12. Westminster	l.	a place noted for drunkenness, riots, and brawling
____13. Lady Jane Grey	m.	tyrannical ruler; loving father
____ 14. Mary	n.	kind guardian; thinks the prince is mad
____15. Father Andrew	o.	friend, protector; may sit in the king's presence
____16. Guildhall	p.	self-sacrificing, loving mother
____17. Nan and Bet	q.	kind, helpful priest who is murdered
____18. Lord St. John	r.	helps the prince; becomes Duke of Somerset
____19. Edith Hendon	s.	prince's kind and loving half-sister
____20. The Ruffler	t.	place where the prince learns of the king's death

B. Multiple Choice: Circle the letter for the BEST answer to each question. (2 pts. each)

21. The Cantys' living conditions are best described as
    (a) affluent and enjoyable
    (b) dismal and wretched
    (c) poor but cheerfully decorated
    (d) middle-class and comfortable

22. At the end of the day, Tom is beaten
    (a) in spite of anything he can do
    (b) because he steals
    (c) because his mother hates him
    (d) if he comes home empty-handed

23. Tom begins to act like a prince because
    (a) he reads and dreams about a princely life
    (b) his father tells him he deserves to be a prince
    (c) Father Andrew tells him he is really the king's son
    (d) he receives an invitation to the palace

24. One primary effect of Tom's dreams of grandeur is
    (a) his plan to sneak into the palace
    (b) the magnification of the wretchedness of his surroundings
    (c) his decision to run away from home
    (d) his desire to become a priest

25. Edward's initial reaction to Tom indicates Edward's
    (a) aversion to poverty
    (b) vindictiveness
    (c) compassion
    (d) desire to have a brother

26. Edward is fascinated by Tom's
    (a) stories of his success as a thief
    (b) stories of his success as a beggar
    (c) tales of his adventures in Scotland
    (d) tales of the exciting life in Offal Court

27. _____ first voices the similarities between Tom and Edward.
    (a) Edward
    (b) Tom
    (c) the Earl of Hertford
    (d) Elizabeth

28. The orphans at Christ's Church
    (a) attempt to help Edward find his way home
    (b) invite Edward to stay with them for awhile
    (c) mock and abuse Edward
    (d) ignore Edward

29. When Tom's father encounters Edward in Offal Court, he
    (a) thinks the boy is crazy
    (b) accuses him of killing Father Andrew
    (c) refuses to allow him to come home
    (d) offers to help him return to the palace

30. When Tom realizes he is mistaken for the prince, he
    (a) becomes determined to hide his true identity
    (b) hides in the closet
    (c) begs to be taken to the king
    (d) tries to explain his true identity

31. King Henry VIII tests the extent of his son's madness with
    (a) questions about the Great Seal
    (b) questions in Latin and French
    (c) questions about the boy's mother
    (d) a session with a psychiatrist

32. The king decides that his son's malady is the result of
    (a) playing outside in the sun too long
    (b) too much idle time
    (c) too much study and confinement
    (d) lack of his father's love

33. The two guardians in the palace who help Tom the most are
    (a) Earl of Hertford/Mary
    (b) Earl of Hertford/St. John
    (c) St. John/Father Andrew
    (d) Elizabeth/Lady Jane Grey

34. The test Tom's mother conducts to prove her son's identity
    (a) fails but she can't give him up
    (b) succeeds but she can't accept it
    (c) fails and she vows to make him leave
    (d) succeeds and gives her total peace of mind

35. The Cantys are forced to leave Offal Court
    (a) because Tom's true identity is detected
    (b) the constable threatens Mr. Canty with imprisonment
    (c) King Henry discovers they have stolen his son
    (d) Mr. Canty kills Father Andrew

36. Edward demands that Miles Hendon do all but which one of the following for him?
    (a) give him his bed
    (b) prepare his food
    (c) stand in his presence
    (d) return him to the palace

37. Miles Hendon reveals to Edward all but which one of the following?
    (a) He has been away from home for ten years.
    (b) His father is a baronet and master of Hendon Hall.
    (c) His brother Arthur is dead.
    (d) He served in the war for three years.

38. Tom's suggested solution to the financial problems of the king's household reveals
    (a) his stinginess/meanness
    (b) his thriftiness/resourcefulness
    (c) a spendthrift, selfish attitude
    (d) his carelessness/unconcern

39. The relationship between Tom and Edward's whipping boy is best described as
    (a) mutual need
    (b) mutual antagonism
    (c) total unconcern
    (d) suppressed anger

40. Tom's compassion toward condemned prisoners results in all but which one of the following?
    (a) The Earl of Hertford is profoundly grateful.
    (b) The court responds with admiration and applause.
    (c) Lord St. John questions Tom's wisdom.
    (d) The court recognizes Tom's wisdom.

41. The gang of which Edward unwillingly becomes a part
    (a) has never actually participated in criminal activity
    (b) is known around the country for kidnapping small children
    (c) decides to disband after realizing Edward is a king
    (d) is a mixture of criminals and victims of Henry VIII's unjust laws

42. The hermit with whom Edward takes refuge proves to be
    (a) angry at Miles Hendon
    (b) crazy and vindictive
    (c) an escaped convict
    (d) on a secret mission for Henry VIII

43. Miles arranges Edward's escape from the court's punishment for stealing a pig by
    (a) threatening to tell the judge about the constable's dishonesty
    (b) bribing the constable with a large sum of money
    (c) revealing Edward's true identity
    (d) blackmailing the judge

44. When Miles Hendon returns to Hendon Hall, all but which one of the following occurs?
    (a) Hugh denies knowing him.
    (b) He learns that Edith is married to Hugh.
    (c) He discovers that all the land has been sold.
    (d) He learns that his father and brother are dead.

45. During Blake Andrews' visits to Miles in prison, he
    (a) tries to get Miles to give him money
    (b) attempts to get Miles to escape
    (c) forces Miles to reveal that he is an imposter
    (d) reveals the truth about the Hendon family.

46. Edward learns from Andrews that
    (a) Tom has been declared an imposter
    (b) King Henry VIII was buried a week before
    (c) the young king is highly respected
    (d) the Earl of Hertford is dead

47. During Tom's brief tenure as king, he does all but which one of the following?
    (a) frees three prisoners from death by execution
    (b) forbids further execution by boiling in oil
    (c) secures teachers for the boys at Christ's Church orphanage
    (d) stops the execution of the Duke of Norfolk

48. When Tom recognizes his mother during the coronation procession, he
    (a) sends his servant to get her
    (b) vows he doesn't know her
    (c) pleads with her to forgive him
    (d) orders her removed from the courtyard

49. Which of the following is NOT revealed at the end of the novel?
    (a) King Edward VI enjoys a long, prosperous reign.
    (b) Miles Hendon receives the title of Earl of Kent.
    (c) Tom Canty receives the title of King's Ward.
    (d) Miles Hendon marries Edith.

50. While roaming the countryside of England as Tom Canty, Edward vows to do all but which one of the following?
    (a) always honor little children
    (b) restore the Ruffler to society
    (c) sweep unjust laws from the statute books
    (d) never forget the scene of the two women who were burned to death

C. Essay: Choose one of the following and respond in a well-developed paragraph of at least five sentences. (10 pts.)

    (a) Explain the importance of loyalty in the novel. Give three specific examples from the novel.

    (b) Characterize Edward. Give specific examples from the novel.

    (c) Characterize Tom. Give specific examples from the novel.

D. Creative Response: Choose one of the following. (10 pts.)

    (a) Write name poems for the following: Miles Hendon, John Canty, Father Andrew.

    (b) Write a eulogy for King Edward VI.

A. Identification: Write the name of the person that best fits the description. (2 pts. each)

1. _____ : an abusive father who forces his children to beg

2. _____ : "Prince of Limitless Plenty"

3. _____ : unkempt, dirty, good-hearted sisters

4. _____ : woman with a wicked, evil heart; a beggar

5. _____ : chief of a gang of ruffians

6. _____ : fun-loving cousin of the prince

7. _____ : manipulative, cruel brother

8. _____ : "Prince of Poverty"

9. _____ : tyrannical ruler; loving father

10. _____ : friend, protector; allowed to sit in the king's presence

11. _____ : self-sacrificing, loving mother

12. _____ : prince's kind and loving half-sister

13. _____ : helps the prince; becomes Duke of Somerset

14. _____ : kind, helpful priest who is murdered

B. Short Answers: Briefly complete each statement. (2 pts. each)

15. The Cantys' living conditions are best described as

16. Father Andrew helps Tom by

17. At the end of the day, Tom is beaten if

18. Tom's dreams about a princely life cause him to

19. Tom and Edward first meet when

20. Edward wants to live Tom's life for one day because

Name _____

21. The orphans at Christ's Church treat Edward

22. When Tom's father finds Edward in Offal Court, he thinks

23. King Henry VIII decides his son's madness is caused by

24. The two guardians who help Tom the most are

25. Tom's mother tests her son's identity by

26. The Cantys are forced to leave Offal Court because

27. Edward demands that Miles Hendon (List at least 2 things.)

28. Edward's whipping boy calls his back his bread because

29. After being recaptured by Tom's father, Edward unwilling joins

30. The hermit with whom Edward takes refuge decides to kill him because

31. When Edward views the deaths of two Baptist women, he vows

32. When Miles returns to Hendon Hall, he discovers (List at least 2 things.)

33. Miles learns the truth about the Hendon family from

34. Edward dubs Miles an "earl" after

35. When Tom sees his mother during the coronation procession, he

36. Tom helps Edward regain his right to the throne by

37. Miles is escorted into the presence of King Edward VI after he gives the guards

38. Two positive things Tom does in his brief tenure as king:

39. Two vows Edward makes while roaming the countryside of England as Tom Canty:

40. Tell at least one thing about each of the following characters at the end of the novel: Edward, Tom, Miles.

C. Essay: Choose one of the following and respond in a well-developed paragraph of at least seven sentences. (10 pts.)

   (a) Explain how Edward changes from the beginning of the novel to the end. What does he learn about the common people? What does he discover about himself? Give specific examples from the novel.

   (b) Explain the importance of Father Andrew's role in Tom's life. How does he help Tom as a child and in his brief role as king?

   (c) Explain the development of the theme of monarchy vs. democracy in the novel.

D. Creative Response: Choose one of the following. (10 pts.)

   (a) Write a brief tale in which you imagine that you and a well-known person briefly exchange identities. Who would you choose? Why? What would you do?

   (b) Write a diamente poem contrasting "Prince" and "Pauper."

   (c) Write an editorial for a newspaper beginning with the phrase, "If I were President of the United States..."

Answer Key

Activities #1 and #2: Responses will vary. **Activity #3:** 1. e 2. i 3. n 4. j 5. c 6. l 7. p 8. s 9. q 10. a 11. m 12. g 13. f 14. r 15. k 16. d 17. t 18. b 19. o 20. h

Activity #4: Charts will vary. Definitions: 1. mummeries: actors in a silent show 2. wenches: girls considered as belonging to the class of workers and peasants 3. commiseration: compassion, sympathy 4. canker: anything that eats away, destroys, or corrupts 5. usurper: one who seizes something wrongfully 6. limpid: clear, transparent 7. rapier: light, pointed sword only for thrusting 8. waif: homeless child; orphan 9. inane: empty, silly, foolish 10. soliloquizing: talking with oneself 11. insolent: insulting, disrespectful 12. alacrity: quickness, alertness 13. suborned: bribed to do evil 14. obsequies: funeral rites or ceremonies 15. preamble: introductory part; preface 16. ducal: of or relating to a duke 17. formidable: to be feared; overpowering 18. veneration: giving reverence, especially to the aged.

Activity #5: Examples will vary. Synonyms: 1. fierce 2. irreverent talk 3. mocking 4. meaningful names 5. Destiny 6. mysterious 7. irritant 8. cows 9. pretty 10. wisdom 11. generous 12. sensibly 13. fathers of families 14. highest-order angel 15. powerless 16. respect 17. thicket 18. humiliation 19. bad

Activity #6: 1. d 2. g 3. i 4. n 5. a 6. h 7. j 8. l 9. k 10. m 11. b 12. e 13. f 14. c

Activity #7: 1. skiing; others refer to respectful bowing 2. wealth; others indicate severe lack of money 3. vessels; others are holders of land in a feudal system 4. money; others mean to tear 5. bigger; others mean to give gifts 6. effort; others indicate a similarity 7. statistic; others mean commendation or praise 8. transfer; others relate to a church 9. natural; others indicate something supernatural 10. treachery; others mean to be faithful 11. powerless; others are hereditary rulers 12. frivolity; others relate to meditating 13. powerful; others indicate sluggishness 14. detrimental; others indicate an agreeable reaction

Note: Student responses to thought questions will vary.
Chapters 1–3: 1. Tom: born to a poor family; unwanted at birth and wrapped in rags; now lives in the impoverished, despicable Offal Court. Edward: son of King Henry VIII; all England rejoiced at his birth; now lives in Westminster palace with hundreds of servants to care for him (pp. 1-3, 9-10) 2. Tom's father John Canty—abusive, a thief; Tom's mother—kind, shares her food with him, consoles him; Tom's grandmother—cruel, a beggar, beats Tom; Tom's twin sisters Nan and Bet—uneducated, kind; all are dirty (pp. 3-5) 3. a poor old priest who teaches Tom to read and write and the right way to live (pp. 4-5) 4. He is not unhappy because he has never known anything different; enjoys playing with his friends; loves to listen to Father Andrew's tales about kings (pp. 4-6) 5. desires to see a real prince; pictures himself living a princely life; dreams of fine people; makes him realize how bad his own surroundings are and causes him to want to be clean and better clothed (pp. 5-7) 6. Tom is traveling around London and comes to Westminster palace; sees the prince who invites him in after the guard tells him to leave (pp. 8-11) 7. Tom: Prince of Poverty; Edward: Prince of Limitless Plenty (p. 10) 8. Tom: his mistreatment by his father and grandmother; the goodness of his mother and sisters; their poverty; his education from Father Andrew. Edward: his father never strikes him but sometimes scolds him; his sister Elizabeth and cousin Jane are happy but his sister Mary is gloomy; wealth of the palace (pp. 9-12) 9. Edward is fascinated with Tom's tales of Offal Court and wants to enjoy being a pauper just once; Tom wants to be clothed like a prince just once. They discover that they look just alike. Edward rushes to the gate to reprimand the guard for hurting Tom; the guard

thinks he is Tom and makes him leave (pp. 13-15) 10. Responses will vary. 11. Activity

Chapters 4–6: 1. The boys mock him, beat him, and set the dogs on him; When he is king, the orphans will have teachers instead of just food and shelter (pp. 17-18). 2. grabs him and threatens to break every bone in his body because he has no money from begging (p. 19) 3. John Canty decides the boy is crazy when he says he is the Prince of Wales; drags him home (p. 19) 4. kindly and gently; assures "Edward" of his love; questions him and decides he is mad but not permanently; orders his guardians to do away with study and involve him in sports (pp. 22-26) 5. Earl of Hertford: Edward's uncle and advisor; St. John: a lord in court; both guide and help Tom in his new role; they help him do the right thing and give the right answers (pp. 28-32) 6. Elizabeth comforts him, encourages him, covers his mistakes; acts as a buffer between Tom and Jane. Jane is loving but not as understanding (pp. 30-32). 7. Activity 8. Activity

Chapters 7–9: 1. Since there is a servant for everything else, he is afraid to scratch his nose because he thinks he might offend the "nose scratcher" (p. 38). 2. to seal his order for the execution of the Duke of Norfolk (pp. 40-42) 3. the Earl of Hertford; doesn't know what it is or where it might be (pp. 40-42) 4. surrounded by servants, magnificently dressed and fed; enjoys great ceremonies (pp. 36-37, 44-46) 5. Responses will vary. 6. Activity

Chapters 10–11: 1. His father and grandmother beat him and mock him; girls are forced to kneel before him; his mother and sisters try to care for him and comfort him (pp. 48-50). 2. startles him to see if he responds as Tom would, by throwing his hand before his eyes with the palm inward; Edward doesn't react as Tom would but she won't accept the result because she can't give him up (pp. 50-52). 3. Father Andrew; John Canty hits him hard and kills him (pp. 53-55). 4. becomes jealous and angry; decides he will allow Tom time for spiritual preparation and then have him hanged, drawn, and quartered for high treason (p. 55) 5. Henry VIII dies (pp. 60-61). 6. Miles Hendon (pp. 61-62) 7. revokes Henry VIII's order for the execution of the Duke of Norfolk (pp. 60-61) 8. Activity

Chapters 12–13: 1. causes him to shudder, cry with bitter grief, and remember his father's kindness and gentleness; feels forsaken (p. 62) 2. Even though he doesn't believe him and thinks he is mad, Miles does what Edward asks: gives him his bed, prepares his food, washes him, and stands in his presence (pp. 65-70). 3. grant him and his heirs forever the right to sit in his presence; grants the request (pp. 72-73) 4. ten years; his father sent him to war, where he served for three years, then was captured and spent seven years in prison (pp. 68-70) 5. He goes with a boy who comes and tells him that Miles needs him (pp. 74-78). 6. Responses will vary. 7. Activity 8. Activity

Chapters 14–16: 1. the Earl of Hertford; conducts himself with dignity and does as he is told (pp. 79-85) 2. suggests that they move to a smaller house (pp. 83-85) 3. receives the whippings the prince deserves for not doing his school work or other misbehavior (pp. 85-87) 4. is glad for the job because it provides income for food and other necessities for him and his family; he must provide for them since his father is dead (pp. 88-89) 5. not to turn him away as whipping boy; vows that the job will be permanent and dubs him "Hereditary Grand Whipping Boy to the royal house of England" (pp. 88-89) 6. man: killing someone with poison; woman and girl: selling themselves to the devil and causing a destructive storm; Tom proves their innocence and releases them (pp. 93-102). 7. There is no real evidence and the man claims to have been rescuing a drowning boy at the time the man died; Tom personally observed the man pulling the boy from the water (pp. 94-97). 8. commands them to pull their stockings off and produce a storm; they can't cause a storm (pp. 98-100) 9. Earl of Hertford is grateful when Tom ends the practice of boiling prisoners in oil; court responds to release of prisoners with admiration and applause for Tom's intelligence and spirit (pp. 98-99) 10. Activity

Chapters 17-18: 1. follows Hugo; John Canty recaptures him and takes him to a gang of ruffians (pp. 108-117). 2. John Hobbs; Jack Hobbs (p. 109) 3. made up of both men and women; some are criminals and some, such as the farmer, are innocent victims of King Henry VIII's laws (pp. 110-117) 4. chief of the gang; saves Edward from being beaten by John Canty (pp. 112-115) 5. Hugo; beg or at least be a decoy for Hugo (pp. 118-119) 6. tells the man Hugo is begging for money that Hugo is a beggar and a thief; Hugo runs away; Edward escapes and spends the night in a barn (pp. 120-121). 7. Responses will vary. 8. Activity 9. Activity

Chapters 19–22: 1. kind to him, feed him; children believe he is a king, mother thinks he's crazy; She attempts to find something he can do well: sweeping the house, scrubbing the dishes, cooking; he can't do anything right (pp. 127-132). 2. woman allows Edward to eat with them even though she thinks they are better than he is; Edward allows the peasants to sit and eat at the same time he does; both think they are stooping to the other's level (p. 131). 3. a priest who was turned out of his church homeless and with no money; thinks he is an archangel but would have been a pope if it hadn't been for King Henry (pp. 136-138) 4. kill him; believes Edward is the king's son and wants revenge against the king (pp. 137-139) 5. says the boy had been there but has gone on an errand for the "archangel"; convinces Miles the sounds he hears, actually Edward, are caused by the wind; goes with Miles to find the boy (pp. 141-143) 6. John Canty and Hugo (p. 144) 7. Edward has been tricked by Hugo into being caught with a stolen pig in his hands (pp. 149-151). 8. Responses will vary. 9. Activity 10. Activity

Chapters 23–26: 1. abide by the laws and submit to the court's authority as he would expect one of his subjects to do (pp. 152-153) 2. because the woman says her pig is worth three shillings and an eightpence and the penalty for stealing anything worth more than 13 pence is hanging; the woman reduces the pig's worth to eightpence (pp. 153-159) 3. that the constable has bought the pig for eightpence after taking advantage of the woman by threatening to disclose her crime of false testimony; the constable gives the pig back to the woman and allows Edward to escape (pp. 157-159) 4. His family will welcome him with thanksgiving, and they will have a joyful reunion (pp. 161-163). 5. Hugh denies knowing Miles and tells him the family received a letter about Miles' death; Edith denies his identity (pp. 163-167). 6. His father and older brother are both dead; Edith is married to Hugh (pp. 164-166). 7. Hugh is master of the region and will tell others that Miles is a mad imposter, no one will defend him, and he will be punished; Hugh is a tyrant and she is his slave (pp. 170-171). 8. Responses will vary. 9. Activity

Chapters 27–29: 1. one week; dirty, crowded, filled with loud criminals (pp. 173-174) 2. a lifelong servant of the Hendons; he does know Miles; Arthur died six years before; his father, Sir Richard, insisted that Edith marry Hugh; Hugh is cruel to Edith and the servants; Edith discovered that Hugh had written the letter about Miles' death (pp. 174-176). 3. A rumor says that the young king is mad; King Henry will be buried in a day or two and the new king will be crowned; Hugh is going to the coronation; the Earl of Hertford is now the Duke of Somerset, Lord Protector; the young king is highly respected (pp. 176-178) 4. They are Baptists; death by burning at the stake (pp. 178-181) 5. feels great sorrow, vows he will never forget the scene and will someday sweep the unjust laws from the statute books (pp. 179-181) 6. must sit in the stocks for two hours; confronts officers and says he is the king; Miles takes Edward's lashes (pp. 183-186). 7. cries and vows he will never forget Miles' loyal deed or those who carry out the punishment; dubs Miles an earl (pp. 183-186) 8. go to London; Sir Humphrey Marlow (pp. 187-189) 9. Responses will vary. 10. Activity

Chapters 30–32: 1. Edward: wanders around the land, dirty, ragged, tired, and poorly fed; mistreated by tramps; imprisoned with thieves and murderers; called an idiot and an imposter. Tom: lives a life of luxury in the palace with hundreds of servants; wonderfully dressed; has delicious food; admired and respected (pp. 190-191) 2. He loves the royal life, enjoys being pampered and having servants to do everything for him; listens to his guardians and makes wise decisions (pp. 191-192) 3. remembers and is concerned about Edward at first and feels guilty and ashamed that he has the prince's life; gradually stops thinking about him. Tom grieves for his mother and sisters at first but shudders at the thought of the three dirty people coming into court; finally almost forgets about them but feels guilty when he does (pp. 191-192) 4. vows he doesn't know her (p. 197) 5. thinks the prince has gone mad again (pp. 198-199) 6. just as the Archbishop lifts the crown over Tom's head; Edward declares that he is the rightful king. Several men grab Edward, but Tom tells everyone the truth about Edward's identity. When the Lord Protector doesn't believe Tom and tells the guards to seize Edward, Tom stamps his foot, then runs to Edward and falls on his knees, swearing loyalty to the real king (pp. 206-207). 7. asks Edward about the location of the Great Seal; can't be located at first but Tom helps Edward remember where he put it; seal is found (pp. 205-211) 8. protects Tom from being punished for impersonating him and reminds the Lord Protector that he could lose the title Tom gave him; treats Tom with affection and honor (pp. 210-211) 9. Activity

Chapter 33–Conclusion: 1. Edward's whipping boy searches for Miles, who discovers the boy is Sir Humphrey Marlow's son. The boy takes a message to Edward but the guards find Miles before he returns. They search him, discover the notes Edward had written earlier, and take the notes to the king. This is the key evidence that identifies Miles. Miles is escorted to the king (pp. 212-217). 2. King Edward VI: corrects many injustices he observed while living as Tom; rules only a few years before his death; remembered for mercy during harsh times. Tom: clothed with quaint but rich garments; commended for his actions while king; becomes head of the body of governors for Christ's Hospital; receives title "King's Ward"; lives to be an old man. Miles: becomes the Earl of Kent; receives gold and land; marries Edith after Hugh dies. Tom's mother and sisters: reunited with Tom; promised perpetual care. Hugh Hendon: stripped of all claims and wealth; ordered to prison but released because Miles and Edith will not testify against him; deserts Edith and goes to the Continents; dies soon after. Edith: marries Miles. John Canty: never heard from again (pp. 217-222) 3. Activity 4. Activity

Note: Student responses to activities #8–#17 will vary. This key gives suggested answers.
Activity #8: Edward the Prince: Acts—orders people around, misbehaves at times since the whipping boy takes punishment, playful with sister and cousins. Feels—loved by his father, respected by servants, sometimes wants more adventure. Looks—magnificent clothing, handsome, healthy. Says— It would be worth his father's kingdom to enjoy life in Offal Court just once; tells Tom to exchange clothes with him and that they look exactly alike. Edward as the Pauper: Acts—continues to act like royalty, becomes angry with those who mistreat others, appreciates Miles' loyalty. Feels—lonely, hungry, afraid at times. Looks—dirty, ragged, hungry. Says—keeps claiming that he is the Prince of Wales and later the king, vows to right many of the wrongs he sees in common people, declares he will be recognized as king.

Activity #9: Tom as the Pauper: Acts—develops princely ways, takes beatings without fighting back, begs only when he has to. Feels—as if he is a prince in his dream world, loved by his mother and sisters, regrets his shabby clothing and dirty body, accepts his life and is not unhappy. Says—tells about the beatings, his father and grandmother are wicked, his mother and sisters are good, tells about fun times in Offal Court. Lives—in a dirty, rundown apartment in Offal Court, off Pudding Lane. Looks— thin, hungry, ragged, often dirty. Others' Actions—father and grandmother beat him; mother and sisters love and comfort him; Edward wants to live Tom's life just once; Father Andrew teaches and cares for him. Tom the Prince: Acts—at first frightened, becomes confident and cheerful, tries to do what is right. Feels—intimidated by all the servants, afraid of King Henry, guilty about Edward, ashamed and guilty about his mother and sisters, relieved to be away from his father and grandmother. Says—revokes execution of the Duke of Norfolk, promises that the whipping boy will always have a job, that the man, woman, and child prisoners are not guilty and can go free. Lives—in Westminster palace in London. Looks—handsome in marvelous clothes, healthy after eating well. Others' Actions— guardians advise him, Edward's father loves him, Elizabeth covers for him, everyone respects him.

Activity #10: Miles Hendon: ovals and rectangles—loyal (keeps his word to Edward, will not allow Andrews to endanger his own life, searches for Edward); brave (fights the mob in Edward's defense, refuses to back down from John Canty, demands retribution from the constable); self-confident (doesn't allow Edward's claims of royalty to intimidate him, vows he will reclaim Hendon Hall, goes to London to seek help from the king); compassionate (rescues Edward from his abusive father, does as Edward asks because he thinks the boy is crazy, takes the lashes for Edward).

Activity #11: Father Andrew: kind, educated, compassionate, loves children; John Canty: cruel, abusive, a thief, dirty; Tom's mother: loving, self-sacrificing, concerned, fearful; Tom's grandmother: dirty, cruel, a beggar, demanding; King Henry VIII: fat, an invalid, tyrannical ruler, loving father; Elizabeth: gentle, helpful, compassionate, loving; Mary: stern, unbending, never smiles; Edith: beautiful, intimidated, afraid, controlled, loving.

Activity #12: Victims: Tom, Father Andrew, Edward, Miles, Edith, Tom's mother, Nan and Bet, the hermit, prisoners falsely accused. Victimizers: John Canty, Tom's grandmother, King Henry VIII, the hermit, the Ruffler and members of his gang, orphans at Christ's Church, the constable, Hugh Hendon. Fighters: Miles Hendon, Edward, members of the gang, orphans at Christ's Church, Tom. Heroes: Miles, Edward, Tom, Father Andrew. Cruel Ones: John Canty, Tom's grandmother, Henry VIII, the hermit, Hugo, Hugh Hendon. Helpful Ones: Tom, Miles, the peasant family, the judge, the lady whose pig is stolen, the Earl of Hertford, St. John, Elizabeth, Jane, Tom's mother and sisters, Blake Andrews.

Activity #13: Title: *The Prince and the Pauper*. Setting, Characters, Problem, Solution: England, 1547; protagonists Tom Canty and Edward Tudor; switched identities, problems each boy encounters, need to correct the mistake; Edward ultimately becomes king, Tom is honored as the king's friend. (1) Tom and Edward are born the same day. (2) The two boys meet accidentally, exchange clothes, and realize they look exactly alike. (3) John Canty finds Edward, thinks he is Tom, and beats him. (4) Miles Hendon rescues Edward. (5) Edward encounters many problems as Tom. (6) Tom becomes Prince of Wales. (7) Tom becomes King of England and conducts himself wisely. (8) Edward reappears on Tom's coronation day, and Tom helps prove the prince's real identity. (9) Edward is crowned King of England and honors all who helped him.

Activity #14: Theme—loyalty; spokes—Miles' toward Edward; Blake Andrews' toward Miles; willingness to take another person's punishment; Tom helps Edward prove his true identity; Edward honors all who helped him; Miles' ability to forgive Edith for denying who he was; Earl of Hertford and St. John as the prince's guardians; Elizabeth covers Tom's mistakes.

Activity #15: Effect: unrest among the common people of England during the reign of Henry VIII. Causes: banishment of priests from churches and monasteries; refusal to allow religious freedom;

unjust treatment of prisoners; inhumane methods of execution; unjust laws such as taking the farmers' land; sumptuous living for monarchy, poverty for many common people.

Activity #16: (1) Tom's birth: rejection, sadness, apathy. (2) Edward's birth: rejoicing, celebrating, excitement. (3) Tom and Edward switch roles: excitement, fear, anticipation, anxiety. (4) John Canty finds Edward: fear, anger, indignation. (5) Miles Hendon rescues Edward: relief, anticipation, thankfulness. (6) Tom becomes king: anxiety, insecurity, determination. (7) Edward reappears on Tom's coronation day: fear, anxiety, excitement, distrust. (8) Edward is crowned king: relief, joy, acceptance, thankfulness.

Activity #17: (1) England (2) Tom, Edward (3) They switch roles. (4) pauper, beggar; prince, wealthy (5) Earl of Hertford, Elizabeth; Miles Hendon, John Canty, the hermit (6) Edward returns, crowned King of England (7) Responses will vary.

Activity #18, Quiz #1: 1. c 2. e 3. a 4. f 5. d 6. b 7. F (pp. 4-5) 8. F (p. 4) 9. T (p. 5) 10. T (pp. 10-11) 11. T (pp. 29-33) 12. T (p. 32) 13. F (pp. 37-39) 14. F (p. 41) 15. T (pp. 22-23)

Activity #19, Quiz #2: 1. Father Andrew (pp. 47, 53) 2. startling him to see if he puts his hand over his eyes as Tom does (pp. 51-52) 3. Miles Hendon (pp. 59, 62) 4. sitting in the king's presence (p. 72) 5. find a smaller house (pp. 83-84) 6. heartbroken, sad (p. 62) 7. F (p. 52) 8. T (pp. 49-50) 9. T (pp. 60-61) 10. F (p. 74) 11. F (pp. 79-80, 85) 12. T (p. 88)

Activity #20, Quiz #3: 1. T (pp. 107-109) 2. F (pp. 113-114) 3. T (pp. 119-120) 4. F (pp. 123-124) 5. F (pp. 127-132) 6. Hobbs (p. 109) 7. the Ruffler (p. 112) 8. Foo-foo the first, king of the Mooncalves (p. 116) 9. the hermit (pp. 133-139) 10. John Canty and Hugo (p. 144)

Activity #21, Quiz #4: 1. a pig (p. 153) 2. changes the value of the pig (pp. 154-155) 3. return the pig to the woman and allow Edward to escape (pp. 157-159) 4. Hendon Hall (p. 162) 5. Edith (pp. 170-171) 6. writes a note in three languages to his uncle Hertford (pp. 168-169) 7. Blake Andrews (pp. 175-177) 8. the two Baptist ladies (pp. 179-181) 9. sweep from the statute books laws that shame England (pp. 178-182) 10. he takes Edward's punishment (pp. 184-186)

Activity #22, Quiz #5: 1. F (pp. 190-191) 2. T (p. 192) 3. T (p. 197) 4. F (p. 199) 5. F (p. 203) 6. T (pp. 205-211) 7. b 8. d 9. e 10. a 11. c (#7–#11, pp. 220-222)

Final Test, Level One: (A) 1. j 2. d 3. a 4. m 5. o 6. k 7. l 8. r 9. p 10. f 11. s 12. c 13. h 14. b 15. q 16. t 17. g 18. n 19. i 20. e (B) 21. b (pp. 3-4) 22. d (p. 4) 23. a (p. 6) 24. b (p. 7) 25. c (p. 10) 26. d (pp. 12-13) 27. a (p. 14) 28. c (pp. 16-17) 29. a (p. 19) 30. d (p. 21) 31. b (pp. 24-25) 32. c (pp. 22-26) 33. b (pp. 28-32) 34. a (pp. 33-35) 35. d (pp. 53-55) 36. d (pp. 72-73) 37. c (pp. 68-70) 38. b (pp. 83-85) 39. a (pp. 85-90) 40. c (pp. 96-102) 41. d (pp. 110-17) 42. b (pp. 133-144) 43. a (pp. 158-159) 44. c (pp. 160-167) 45. d (pp. 173-176) 46. c (pp. 176-178) 47. c (pp. 191-192) 48. b (pp. 195-199) 49. a (pp. 217-222) 50. b (throughout) (C & D) Responses will vary.

Final Test, Level Two: (A) 1. John Canty 2. Edward Tudor 3. Nan and Bet 4. Tom's grandmother 5. The Ruffler 6. Lady Jane Grey 7. Hugh Hendon 8. Tom Canty 9. King Henry VIII 10. Miles Hendon 11. Tom's mother 12. Elizabeth 13. Earl of Hertford 14. Father Andrew (B) 15. miserable, dismal, wretched, dirty (pp. 3-4) 16. giving him a place of refuge, being his friend, teaching him (p. 4) 17. he comes home empty-handed (p. 4) 18. begin to act like a prince (p. 6) 19. Tom goes to the gate of the palace (p. 7) 20. Tom's life in Offal Court sounds exciting with entertainment, fights, and playing (pp. 12-13) 21. abusively—mock him, beat him, set the dogs on him (pp. 17-18) 22. the boy is crazy (p. 19) 23. too much study and confinement (pp. 24-25) 24. Earl of Hertford and Lord St. John (pp. 28-32) 25. startling him to see if he throws his hand in front of his eyes as Tom does (pp. 33-35) 26. John Canty kills Father Andrew (pp. 53-55) 27. give him his bed, prepare his food, stand in his presence (pp. 72-73) 28. if he isn't whipped, he has no money to buy bread (pp. 86-88) 29. a gang of ruffians (pp. 110-114) 30. he believes Edward is the prince and wants revenge for King Henry VIII's mistreatment of him and other priests (pp. 137-138) 31. never to forget the sight and to sweep unjust laws from the statute books of England (pp. 180-182) 32. his father and brother are dead, Edith is Hugh's wife, all the loyal servants are gone, Hugh has control of the estate (pp. 160-167) 33. Blake Andrews (pp. 173-176) 34. Miles takes Edward's lashes (pp. 185-186) 35. vows he doesn't know her (p. 197) 36. helping him remember where he put the Great Seal (pp. 205-211) 37. the notes Edward wrote to the Earl of Hertford (pp. 215-217) 38. frees three prisoners from death by execution, stops the execution of the Duke of Norfolk, forbids further executions by boiling in oil (pp. 60, 96-102) 39. to always honor children, to provide teachers for the orphans at Christ's Church, to sweep unjust laws from the statute books of England (pp. 16-17, 129, 179-181) 40. Edward: rules for only a few years before his death; rights many of the injustices he observed. Tom: receives title of "King's Ward," is made chief officer over Christ's Hospital, lives to be an old man. Miles: receives title of Earl of Kent, gets gold and land, marries Edith (pp. 217-222) **(C & D)** Responses will vary.

Notes

48